LEGO NINJAGO®
Masters of Spinjitzu

NINJA VS. SKY PIRATES

WRITTEN BY
CLAIRE SIPI

TAKE TO THE SKY

IN THE SIXTH SEASON of NINJAGO®: Masters of Spinjitzu the ninja are superstars—appearing in their own TV show and adored by fans. But danger is looming, with the escape of notorious djinn Nadakhan, and his rowdy crew—the Sky Pirates! With an evil djinn on the scene, the ninja must be careful what they wish for... A total of seven LEGO® sets bring the battle to life!

HOW TO USE THIS BOOK

This book is a guideto the LEGO® NINJAGO® minifigures of Season 6. Learn all about the Sky Pirates and the amazing new fighting skills that the Ninja must learn in order to defeat them.

To find out more about this minifigure see p.10.

CONTENTS

LLOYD

MASTER-IN-TRAINING

NINJA FILE

LIKES: Further training
DISLIKES: Being famous
FRIENDS: Reliable Cole
FOES: Monkey Wretch
SKILLS: Self-control
GEAR: Golden weapon staff

SET NAME: Sky Pirate Jet, Misfortune's Keep
SET NUMBER: 70601, 70605
YEAR: 2016

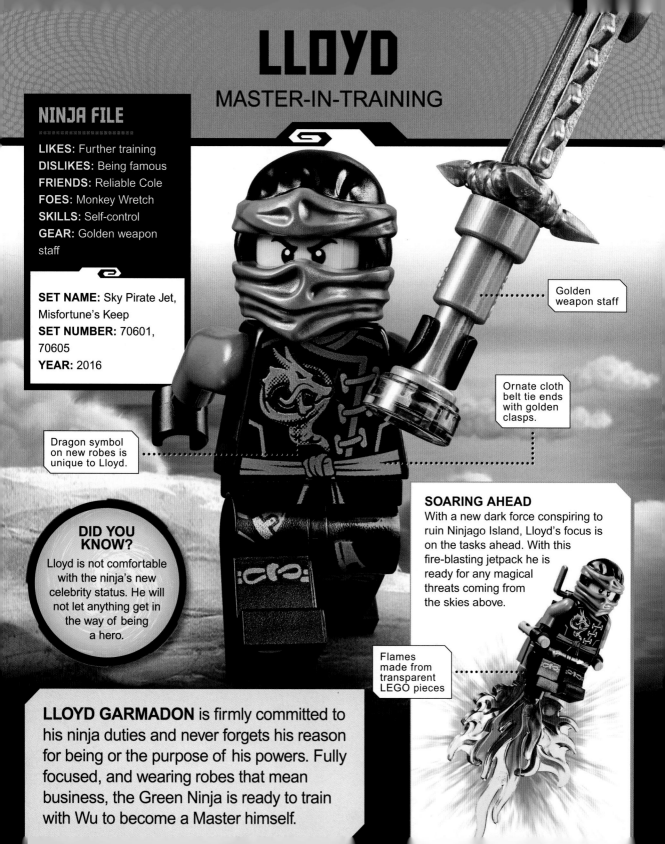

Golden weapon staff

Ornate cloth belt tie ends with golden clasps.

Dragon symbol on new robes is unique to Lloyd.

DID YOU KNOW?

Lloyd is not comfortable with the ninja's new celebrity status. He will not let anything get in the way of being a hero.

SOARING AHEAD

With a new dark force conspiring to ruin Ninjago Island, Lloyd's focus is on the tasks ahead. With this fire-blasting jetpack he is ready for any magical threats coming from the skies above.

Flames made from transparent LEGO pieces

LLOYD GARMADON is firmly committed to his ninja duties and never forgets his reason for being or the purpose of his powers. Fully focused, and wearing robes that mean business, the Green Ninja is ready to train with Wu to become a Master himself.

COLE
LIVING GHOST

Face now a ghostly green color

NINJA FILE

LIKES: Pulling Jay's leg
DISLIKES: Thermal vision
FRIENDS: Serious Lloyd
FOES: Dogshank
SKILLS: Quick thinking
GEAR: Katanas, scythe

SET NAME: Cole's Dragon, Tiger Widow Island
SET NUMBER: 70599, 70604
YEAR: 2016

DID YOU KNOW?

As a ghost, Cole has had to learn how to make physical contact with objects and how to move through walls.

Silver arms match head wrap and belt tie.

GHOST DRAGON RIDER

Even as a ghost, Cole is an awesome ninja. With Master Wu's guidance, he has learnt to control his elemental earth powers, and can call upon his ghost dragon in battle. This new beast is small but snappy!

WITH THE HELP of his friends and Wu, Cole is learning to accept his new living ghost form. The journey has not been easy, but Cole has tapped into his true ninja essence and confronted his despair and fears. He is now ready to face the new ghostly challenges ahead of him.

WELCOME TO DJINJAGO!

DJINJAGO IS A MAGICAL PLACE MADE OF FLOATING SKY ISLANDS

HOME TO DJINNS, WHO HAVE THE POWER TO GRANT WISHES

NOTORIOUS BY NATURE, DJINNS TWIST THE WORDS OF EVERY WISH

THEY FULFILL THE WISH BUT DO SO BY RUINING SOMETHING ELSE

ZANE
NINDROID BROTHER-IN-ARMS

Zane's rebuilt Nindroid headpiece with cybernetic eye

New Skybound ninja robe shows a whirlwind-style emblem representing Zane's elemental ice powers.

Single pauldron allows for freer movement in battle.

NINJA FILE

LIKES: Mini-droid chess
DISLIKES: Hackers who invade his system
FRIENDS: Jay
FOES: Fickle Ronin
SKILLS: Logical thinking
GEAR: Golden katanas

SET NAME: Raid Zeppelin
SET NUMBER: 70603
YEAR: 2016

ICY FLYER
Sitting at the controls of his super cool shuriken-style hover battle machine, Zane calculates the right moment to strike, and then speedily and stealthily zooms up on his enemies.

A pair of katanas can still be slotted into the ninja's new back piece.

FULLY REBOOTED and functioning at maximum Nindroid capacity, Zane is glad to be back with his team, training and refining his ninja skills. Being a Nindroid, Zane's not really fazed by the group's sudden celebrity—he'd rather be computing his battle strategies!

LIKES: Gushing fangirls
DISLIKES: Serving prison time in Kryptarium
FRIENDS: Cole
FOES: Sqiffy
SKILLS: Pulling a ruse
GEAR: Golden katanas

SET NAME: Ninja Bike Chase, Misfortune's Keep
SET NUMBER: 70600, 70605
YEAR: 2016

Two-tone colored head wrap

DID YOU KNOW?

Now that the team has achieved celebrity status, action figure toys of each of the ninja have hit the stores across Ninjago Island!

Three clasps fasten the side of the new Skybound robes.

Ornate knee-ties secure robes.

SUPER BIKE

This magnificent bike with its all-terrain giant wheels is certainly fit for a celeb! Whether cruising round town waving to adoring fans, or chasing evil Sky Pirates, Kai has the skills to handle this awesome ninja machine.

LOOK FOR THE CROWDS of adoring fans and the Master of Fire is sure to be at the center of all the attention. Kai loves being a celebrity. Let's hope that with his famous hot temper, he doesn't become a ninja diva, or he might forget what his real job is!

JAY
HEROIC NINJA

NINJA FILE

LIKES: Helping his ninja friends
DISLIKES: Making a wish!
FRIENDS: Zane
FOES: Nadakhan
SKILLS: Saving his friends
GEAR: Golden katanas

SET NAME: Jay's Elemental Dragon, Misfortune's Keep
SET NUMBER: 70602, 70605
YEAR: 2016

Jay's regular face peeks out from beneath this side of his head wrap.

DID YOU KNOW?
Jay has discovered that he was adopted and that his true father was a famous actor, and also his movie idol!

Like those of his fellow ninja, Jay's outfit is accessorized with black gi and gloves.

SHIVER ME TIMBERS!
When the evil Nadakhan and his fearsome band of Sky Pirates kidnap Jay, he craftily disguises himself as one of the brigands to try and make his escape before they force him to walk the plank.

Eye patch over one eye completes Jay's disguise.

CREATIVE JAY enjoys solving problems. But when it comes to love, none of Jay's inventions can fix his heartbreak. When Nya tells Jay that she only wants to be friends with him, the distraught ninja is tempted by the evil djinn's dark wishes. However, he soon discovers that you can't wish for love.

JAY'S DRAGON
HYDRO-ELECTRIC BEAST

NINJA FILE

LIKES: Mixing things up
DISLIKES: Pirates
FRIENDS: Jay, Nya
FOES: Cyren
SKILLS: Coming up with contingency plans
GEAR: Golden sai

SET NAME: Jay's Elemental Dragon
SET NUMBER: 70602
YEAR: 2016

Tail, legs, feet, and wings are all articulated with ball-and-socket joints.

Eyes made from trans-orange bricks

DRAGON'S HEAD
The dragon's scary-looking head, with fang-filled jaws that open and close, has an articulated neck piece for full movement.

WHEN JAY AND NYA fall from Nadakhan's pirate ship, *Misfortune's Keep*, the two ninja combine their elemental powers—water and lightning—to create this dragon. The resulting creature sizzles with lightning bolts and water power.

NINJA FILE

LIKES: Being part of a team
DISLIKES: Not being taken seriously
FRIENDS: Master Wu
FOES: Dogshank
SKILLS: Fighting Sky Pirates
GEAR: Golden katanas

SET NAME: Ninja Bike Chase, Jay's Elemental Dragon, Tiger Widow Island
SET NUMBER: 70600, 70602, 70604
YEAR: 2016

Deep red color is iconic to Nya.

New emblem in the blue color of Nya's water element decorates her robes.

MISSION POSSIBLE

Without his Djinn Blade, Nadakhan is not so powerful. If Nya and Wu can steal the magical weapon, they just might be able to save the spirits trapped inside it.

AFTER MONTHS of intense training with Wu, Nya is now a fully-fledged Master of Water and part of the team. But she is fed up with all of the attention that the boys get and wants to be recognized for her skills in her own right. Time for Nya to strike out on her own!

STONE WARRIOR JAY
EXCLUSIVE ARMOR

Double-sided face has raised eyebrows that look worried, instead of cross, on the reverse.

NINJA FILE

LIKES: Reading comics

DISLIKES: Days when the comic-book store is closed

FRIENDS: Stone Warrior ninja

FOES: Nindroids

SKILLS: Speed-reading

GEAR: Silver katanas

SET NAME: DK's LEGO® NINJAGO® *Character Encyclopedia: Updated and Expanded*

YEAR: 2016

DID YOU KNOW?

The Stone Warrior armor was first seen in Episode 34, *The Titanium Ninja*, of the NINJAGO®: Masters of Spinjitzu TV series.

Fabric straps join with metal armor in the center of Jay's torso.

Two silver katanas are held in Jay's back pauldrons.

STARFARER

Jay's favorite comic, *Starfarer*, is represented in a simple LEGO tile. Jay idolizes the action hero who stars on its pages, and it might be Jay's destiny to share more than just a love of adventure with the famous Fritz Donnegan!

WEARING HIS Stone Warrior armor, Jay is ready to embark on adventures and emulate his favorite action hero—Fritz Donnegan. In this solid silver armor, Jay can take on any foe, and can join Lloyd, Zane and Kai, who have appeared in minifigure form in this armor, too.

TO BECOME A
TRUE NINJA YOU MUST:

FIND AND CONTROL YOUR ELEMENT

ALWAYS BE LOYAL TO YOUR FRIENDS

LEARN TO WIELD MANY TYPES OF WEAPONS

MASTER THE ART OF STEALTH

NADAKHAN
CAPTAIN OF THE SKY PIRATES

NINJA FILE

LIKES: Breaking apart Ninjago Island
DISLIKES: Failing his father
FRIENDS: Sky Pirates
FOES: Ninja
SKILLS: Granting wishes
GEAR: Djinn Blade

SET NAME: Misfortune's Keep
SET NUMBER: 70605
YEAR: 2016

Genie-style hairpiece

Sky Pirate skull-and-crossbones emblem

DID YOU KNOW?
The Djinn Blade belongs to the royal family of Djinjago. It can trap spirits inside of it, providing power to the wielder.

Extra torso incorporates two extra arms.

Studded belt to match armour

Standard LEGO pirate hook hand

Transparent orange genie tail

TRANSFORMATIVE POWERS
Monkey Wretch was once a skilled human ship mechanic, before Nadakhan tricked him into wishing for more hands and more speed, and turned him into a mechanical monkey. Wretch does all the general repairs on Nadakhan's ship, *Misfortune's Keep*.

NADAKHAN, PRINCE OF DJINJAGO, is a djinn, a magical being who can grant wishes. He blames the ninja for the destruction of his homeland, Djinjago, and with his motley pirate crew in tow, he is now seeking revenge.

CLANCEE
SERPENTINE SKY PIRATE

NINJA FILE

LIKES: Swabbing the deck
DISLIKES: Heights, the sea
FRIENDS: Still looking
FOES: All of Captain Nadakhan's enemies
SKILLS: Evading traps
GEAR: Mop

SET NAME: Raid Zeppelin
SET NUMBER: 70603
YEAR: 2016

Padded shoulder pauldrons

Serpentine snake head with fangs

DID YOU KNOW?
Poor Clancee gets seasick and airsick—not great when you're a pirate sailing the high seas or whizzing through the air on a flying boat!

Rusty body armor and strap with ragged shirt displaying Sky Pirate emblem

Simple, brown wooden peg leg

WISHFUL THINKING
Clancee may not be the brightest crew member, but he knows Nadakhan is not to be trusted. By not asking for a wish, Clancee has probably, without even knowing it, saved his own scaly skin!

HOW THIS nervous Serpentine ended up as part of the crew on *Misfortune's Keep* is anyone's guess, but peg-legged Clancee is content to live the life of a pirate, even though he gets the worst jobs. He is often found mopping down the decks and cleaning up after his shipmates.

FLINTLOCKE

SKY PIRATE FIRST MATE

Pilot goggles worn on top of green flying helmet

Separate bushy mustache piece

DID YOU KNOW?

Flintlocke pilots the sleek Sky Shark jet, which serves as an advance scout for the *Misfortune's Keep*.

Flintlocke wields two pirate pistols at once.

Mismatched legs (one brown, one orange), covered in armor plating, straps and buckles.

NINJA FILE

LIKES: His Sky Shark
DISLIKES: Secrets
FRIENDS: Nadakhan
FOES: Lloyd
SKILLS: Inspiring his crew to charge into battle
GEAR: Pistols

SET NAME: Sky Shark, Misfortune's Keep
SET NUMBER: 70601, 70605
YEAR: 2016

SKY SHARK

With Flintlocke at the helm, this battle jet searches the skies for enemy aircraft. It then slices through sail and steel with its anchor-shaped wings, before the *Misfortune's Keep* arrives.

Hidden dynamite

FLINTLOCKE is Nadakhan's trusted right-hand man. He's loyal to his djinn captain and will follow him anywhere—as long as he knows where they're heading. But if he's expecting his leader to return his loyalty, then he's on the wrong ship!

DOGSHANK

HULKING SKY PIRATE

Horned helmet comes complete with built-in mouth visor, spiked pauldron, and skull emblem.

NINJA FILE

LIKES: Fair fights
DISLIKES: Flintlocke's jokes
FRIENDS: Monkey Wretch
FOES: Nya
SKILLS: Twirling her anchor dangerously on a chain
GEAR: Ship's anchor

SET NAME: Tiger Widow Island
SET NUMBER: 70604
YEAR: 2016

Oversized bigfig hands can clutch weapons.

ON TIGER WIDOW ISLAND
Will Nya's stealthy ninja battle skills be enough to combat the brute strength and size of Dogshank? The pirate swings her weapon of choice, an anchor and chain, at the Master of Water as they fight.

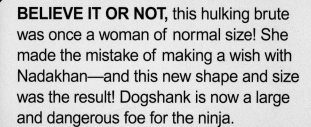

BELIEVE IT OR NOT, this hulking brute was once a woman of normal size! She made the mistake of making a wish with Nadakhan—and this new shape and size was the result! Dogshank is now a large and dangerous foe for the ninja.

NINJA FILE

LIKES: Masks
DISLIKES: Talking
FRIENDS: Sqiffy
FOES: Jay
SKILLS: Spinjitzu
GEAR: Pirate swords

SET NAME: Raid Zeppelin
SET NUMBER: 70603
YEAR: 2016

Horns top Doubloon's samurai-style helmet.

Long fangs curl in sinister fashion up the sides of Doubloon's face.

Red face markings add sinister element

Doubloon, Cyren and Bucko have the same chest armor printed on their torsos.

RAID ZEPPELIN

Behind the wheel of his Raid Zepplin, the silent Doubloon fires the bow-mounted cannon at the enemy. The mid-sized ship, held aloft by gas bags filled with hot air, is one of the Sky Pirates' most potent weapons.

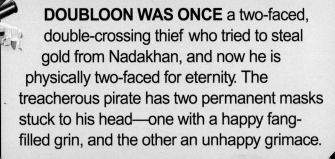

DOUBLOON WAS ONCE a two-faced, double-crossing thief who tried to steal gold from Nadakhan, and now he is physically two-faced for eternity. The treacherous pirate has two permanent masks stuck to his head—one with a happy fang-filled grin, and the other an unhappy grimace.

SQIFFY
SMELLY SKY PIRATE

NINJA FILE

LIKES: Fierce pirate names
DISLIKES: Being the new guy in the crew
FRIENDS: Flintlocke, Doubloon
FOES: Kai
SKILLS: Pestering ninja
GEAR: Pirate sword

SET NAME: Ninja Bike Chase, Ninja Island
SET NUMBER: 70600, 70604
YEAR: 2016

DID YOU KNOW?
Sqiffy's real name is Colin. Nadakhan didn't feel that "Colin" was a proper pirate's name so he changed it to "Sqiffy."

Eye patch just visible beneath head scarf

Unusually, Sqiffy has one yellow arm and one orange arm.

Sqiffy's torso bears a looser uniform to the armor worn by the other pirates.

Sqiffy sports identical legs to Doubloon and Cyren, but the opposite way round to Flintlocke and Bucko.

SKY GLIDER
Armed with weapons and designed for quick turns and rapid ascent, these pirate gliders have enough power to bring down a bigger vessel. Sqiffy skillfully flies it to team up with other pirate gliders—together they can launch a more effective raid on the enemy.

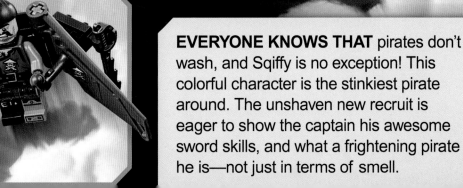

EVERYONE KNOWS THAT pirates don't wash, and Sqiffy is no exception! This colorful character is the stinkiest pirate around. The unshaven new recruit is eager to show the captain his awesome sword skills, and what a frightening pirate he is—not just in terms of smell.

CYREN

SINGING SKY PIRATE

NINJA FILE

LIKES: Applause
DISLIKES: Missing an opportunity to sing
FRIENDS: Bucko
FOES: Cole
SKILLS: Sending people into a trance with her singing
GEAR: Serrated sword

SET NAME: Jay Dragon
SET NUMBER: 70602
YEAR: 2016

Headpiece shows angry facial expression, with a beauty spot and eye patch.

Two belts cross standard Sky Pirate torso.

Standard-issue brown pirate gloves

SINGING RAIDS

Cyren can't perform on stage any more, but she can use her secret weapon on a glider raid. One quick tune and the enemy is brought to their knees. She deserves some applause for that party trick!

CYREN IS ANOTHER VICTIM of one of Nadakhan's twisted wishes. She wanted to be the greatest singer in the world, but instead, the Djinn made her voice capable of temporarily sending humans into a catatonic trance. Not a great career move!

BUCKO

IT'S A PIRATE'S LIFE FOR HIM

NINJA FILE

LIKES: The Raid Zeppelin
DISLIKES: Being bullied by fellow pirates
FRIENDS: Doubloon
FOES: Cole
SKILLS: Growling fiercely
GEAR: Djinn Blade

SET NAME: Cole Mini Dragon, Misfortune's Keep
SET NUMBER: 70599, 70605
YEAR: 2016

Pirate head scarf matches Sqiffy's, but worn at a different angle.

Makeshift eye patch covers Bucko's left eye.

DID YOU KNOW?

Bucko's real name is Landon. But like Colin, Nadakhan didn't think it was a good pirate name, so he changed it.

Orange is Bucko's favorite color!

BLADE BATTLES

Bucko is a skilled swordsman, but he's happy to use any weapon to hand in a battle. Here he has a strong hold on a Djinn Blade, so the ninja will have to fight hard to take it from him.

Djinn Blade with white and blue attachments

THE FIERY, RED-BEARDED BUCKO is another new recruit to Nadakhan's pirate crew. He is a strong and a fearless fighter and follows orders without question—just the kind of shipmate that Nadakhan likes. Bucko is more than eager to do the manipulative Djinn's dirty work.

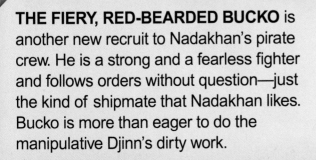

ON TIGER WIDOW ISLAND:

FIGHT OFF ATTACKING SKY PIRATES

BEWARE: POISONOUS SPIDERS!

FIND A SAFE CAVE TO HIDE IN

WATCH OUT FOR FALLING COCONUTS

DK | Penguin Random House

Project Editor Emma Grange
Senior Designers Jo Connor, Mark Penfound
Editors Arushi Vats, Rosie Peet, Matt Jones, Clare Millar
Designers Radhika Banerjee, Dimple Vohra,
Stefan Georgiou
Editorial Assistant Beth Davies
Pre-Production Producer Kavita Varma
Senior Producer Lloyd Robertson
Editorial Managers Paula Regan,
Chitra Subramanyam
Design Managers Guy Harvey, Jo Connor, Neha Ahuja
Creative Manager Sarah Harland
Publisher Julie Ferris
Art Director Lisa Lanzarini
Publishing Director Simon Beecroft

This edition published in 2017
First American Edition, 2016
Published in the United States by DK Publishing
345 Hudson Street, New York, New York 10014
DK, a Division of Penguin Random House LLC

Contains content previously published in LEGO®
NINJAGO® *Character Encyclopedia Updated and Expanded
Edition* (2016)

003–298874–Jul/17

ISBN: 978-5-0010-1402-7
Printed in Heshan, China

ACKNOWLEDGEMENTS
DK would like to thank Randi Sørensen, Martin Leighton Lindhart,
Paul Hansford, Madeline Boushie, Simon Lucas, Nicolaas Johan Bernardo
Vás, and Daniel McKenna at the LEGO Group, Gary Ombler for extra
photography, Andy Jones for extra editorial help, Sam Bartlett for
design assistance and Claire Sipi for her writing. For the original edition
of this book, DK would like to thank Shari Last, Julia March, Ruth Amos,
Lauren Rosier, Mark Richards, Jon Hall, Clive Savage,
Ron Stobbart, and Catherine Saunders.
www.LEGO.com

www.dk.com
A WORLD OF IDEAS:
SEE ALL THERE IS TO KNOW